Prayer Journal for Women:

52 Week Scripture, Notebook, and Devotional for Women of God

© 2021 Silvia Ghiduc

Scripture quotations marked (NIV) are taken from the Holy Bible, New International Version®, NIV® Copyright ©1973, 1978, 1984, 2011 by Biblica, Inc.® Used by permission. All rights reserved worldwide.

ISBN: 978-1-7356426-1-1

Printed and Bound in the United States

This book belongs to

> For I know the plans I have for you, "declares the LORD," plans to prosper you and not to harm you, plans to give you hope and a future. – Jeremiah 29:11

Teach me

I am thankful for

Prayer requests

Date

Answered Prayers

Date

Things on my heart

Highlights of this week

_____
_____
_____
_____
_____
_____
_____
_____

> *I have told you these things, so that in me you may have peace. In this world you will have trouble. But take heart! I have overcome the world. – John 16:33*

Teach me

_____
_____
_____
_____
_____
_____
_____
_____
_____
_____

I am thankful for

_____
_____
_____
_____
_____
_____
_____
_____

Prayer requests

Date

Answered Prayers

Date

Things on my heart

Highlights of this week

_____   _____

_____   _____

_____   _____

_____   _____

_____   _____

_____   _____

_____   _____

> Trust in the LORD with all your heart and lean not on your own understanding; in all your ways submit to him, and he will make your paths straight. – Proverbs 3:5-6

Teach me

_____
_____
_____
_____
_____
_____
_____
_____
_____
_____

I am thankful for

_____
_____
_____
_____
_____
_____
_____
_____
_____

Prayer requests

Date

Answered Prayers

Date

Things on my heart

_____

_____

_____

_____

_____

_____

_____

Highlights of this week

_____

_____

_____

_____

_____

_____

_____

> The LORD is my rock, my fortress and my deliverer; my God is my rock, in whom I take refuge, my shield and the horn of my salvation, my stronghold. – Psalm 18:2

Teach me

_____
_____
_____
_____
_____
_____
_____
_____
_____
_____
_____

I am thankful for

_____
_____
_____
_____
_____
_____
_____
_____
_____

Prayer requests

Date

Answered Prayers

Date

Things on my heart

_____

_____

_____

_____

_____

_____

_____

Highlights of this week

_____

_____

_____

_____

_____

_____

_____

And my God will meet all your needs according to the riches of his glory in Christ Jesus. – Philippians 4:19

Teach me

_____
_____
_____
_____
_____
_____
_____
_____
_____
_____

I am thankful for

_____
_____
_____
_____
_____
_____
_____
_____
_____

Prayer requests

Date

Answered Prayers

Date

Things on my heart

Highlights of this week

————————————————————————

————————————————————————

————————————————————————

————————————————————————

————————————————————————

————————————————————————

————————————————————————

————————————————————————

————————————————————————

————————————————————————

————————————————————————

————————————————————————

————————————————————————

————————————————————————

Praise be to the God and Father of our Lord Jesus Christ, the Father of compassion and the God of all comfort, who comforts us in all our troubles, so that we can comfort those in any trouble with the comfort we ourselves receive from God. – 2 Corinthians 1:3-4

Teach me

I am thankful for

Prayer requests

Date

Answered Prayers

Date

Things on my heart

_____

_____

_____

_____

_____

_____

_____

Highlights of this week

_____

_____

_____

_____

_____

_____

_____

> *I pray that out of his glorious riches he may strengthen you with power through his Spirit in your inner being*
> *– Ephesians 3:16*

Teach me

_____
_____
_____
_____
_____
_____
_____
_____
_____
_____

I am thankful for

_____
_____
_____
_____
_____
_____
_____
_____
_____

Prayer requests

Date

Answered Prayers

Date

Things on my heart

Highlights of this week

_____   _____

_____   _____

_____   _____

_____   _____

_____   _____

_____   _____

_____   _____

> Yet you, LORD, are our Father. We are the clay, you are the potter; we are all the work of your hand.
> – Isaiah 64:8

Teach me

_____
_____
_____
_____
_____
_____
_____
_____
_____
_____
_____
_____

I am thankful for

_____
_____
_____
_____
_____
_____
_____
_____
_____
_____
_____

Prayer requests

Date

Answered Prayers

Date

Things on my heart

_____

_____

_____

_____

_____

_____

_____

Highlights of this week

_____

_____

_____

_____

_____

_____

_____

> But you are a chosen people, a royal priesthood, a holy nation, God's special possession, that you may declare the praises of him who called you out of darkness into his wonderful light.
>
> – 1 Peter 2:9

Teach me

_____
_____
_____
_____
_____
_____
_____
_____
_____
_____

I am thankful for

_____
_____
_____
_____
_____
_____
_____
_____
_____
_____

Prayer requests

Date

Answered Prayers

Date

Things on my heart

Highlights of this week

_____   _____
_____   _____
_____   _____
_____   _____
_____   _____
_____   _____
_____   _____

Week of

> So do not fear, for I am with you; do not be dismayed, for I am your God. I will strengthen you and help you; I will uphold you with my righteous right hand. – Isaiah 41:10

Teach me

I am thankful for

Prayer requests

Date

Answered Prayers

Date

Things on my heart   ## Highlights of this week

_____   _____

_____   _____

_____   _____

_____   _____

_____   _____

_____   _____

_____   _____

_____   _____

Do not be anxious about anything, but in every situation, by prayer and petition, with thanksgiving, present your requests to God. And the peace of God, which transcends all understanding, will guard your hearts and your minds in Christ Jesus. – Philippians 4:6-7

Teach me

_____
_____
_____
_____
_____
_____
_____
_____
_____
_____
_____

I am thankful for

_____
_____
_____
_____
_____
_____
_____
_____
_____
_____
_____

Prayer requests

Date

Answered Prayers

Date

Things on my heart

_____

_____

_____

_____

_____

_____

_____

Highlights of this week

_____

_____

_____

_____

_____

_____

_____

> *Let us then approach God's throne of grace with confidence, so that we may receive mercy and find grace to help us in our time of need. – Hebrew 4:16*

Teach me

_____
_____
_____
_____
_____
_____
_____
_____
_____
_____

I am thankful for

_____
_____
_____
_____
_____
_____
_____
_____
_____

Prayer requests

Date

Answered Prayers

Date

Things on my heart

Highlights of this week

_____

_____

_____

_____

_____

_____

_____

> I delight greatly in the LORD; my soul rejoices in my God. For he has clothed me with garments of salvation and arrayed me in a robe of his righteousness, as a bridegroom adorns his head like a priest, and as a bride adorns herself with her jewels. – Isaiah 61:10

Teach me

_____
_____
_____
_____
_____
_____
_____
_____
_____
_____
_____

I am thankful for

_____
_____
_____
_____
_____
_____
_____
_____
_____
_____

Prayer requests

Date

Answered Prayers

Date

Things on my heart

Highlights of this week

> Be strong and courageous. Do not be afraid or terrified because of them, for the LORD your God goes with you; he will never leave you nor forsake you. – Deuteronomy 31:6

Teach me

_____
_____
_____
_____
_____
_____
_____
_____
_____
_____

I am thankful for

_____
_____
_____
_____
_____
_____
_____
_____
_____
_____
_____

Prayer requests

Date

Answered Prayers

Date

Things on my heart

Highlights of this week

_____   _____

_____   _____

_____   _____

_____   _____

_____   _____

_____   _____

_____   _____

> Yet I am always with you; you hold me by my right hand. You guide me with your counsel, and afterward you will take me into glory. – Psalm 73:23-24

Teach me

_____
_____
_____
_____
_____
_____
_____
_____
_____
_____

I am thankful for

_____
_____
_____
_____
_____
_____
_____
_____
_____
_____

Prayer requests

Date

Answered Prayers

Date

Things on my heart

Highlights of this week

_____   _____

_____   _____

_____   _____

_____   _____

_____   _____

_____   _____

_____   _____

> Many are the plans in a person's heart, but it is the LORD's purpose that prevails. – Proverbs 19:21

Teach me

I am thankful for

Prayer requests

Date

Answered Prayers

Date

Things on my heart

Highlights of this week

_____

_____

_____

_____

_____

_____

_____

_____

_____

_____

_____

_____

_____

_____

> This is what the LORD says-- your Redeemer, the Holy One of Israel: "I am the LORD your God, who teaches you what is best for you, who directs you in the way you should go.
>
> – Isaiah 48:17

Teach me

I am thankful for

Prayer requests

Date

Answered Prayers

Date

Things on my heart

_____

_____

_____

_____

_____

_____

_____

Highlights of this week

_____

_____

_____

_____

_____

_____

_____

You make known to me the path of life; you will fill me with joy in your presence, with eternal pleasures at your right hand.

– Psalm 16:11

Teach me

I am thankful for

Prayer requests

Date

Answered Prayers

Date

Things on my heart

Highlights of this week

_____
_____
_____
_____
_____
_____
_____
_____

_____
_____
_____
_____
_____
_____
_____
_____

> *Let us fix our eyes on Jesus, the author and perfecter of our faith, who for the joy set before Him endured the cross, scorning its shame, and sat down at the right hand of the throne of God.*
> *– Hebrew 12:2*

Teach me

_____
_____
_____
_____
_____
_____
_____
_____
_____
_____
_____

I am thankful for

_____
_____
_____
_____
_____
_____
_____
_____
_____
_____
_____

Prayer requests

Date

Answered Prayers

Date

Things on my heart

Highlights of this week

_____

_____

_____

_____

_____

_____

_____

Blessed are those who have learned to acclaim you, who walk in the light of your presence, LORD. – Psalm 89:15

Teach me

I am thankful for

Prayer requests

Date

Answered Prayers

Date

Things on my heart

Highlights of this week

_____   _____

_____   _____

_____   _____

_____   _____

_____   _____

_____   _____

_____   _____

> Your word is a lamp for my feet, a light on my path.
> – Psalm 119:105

Teach me

_____
_____
_____
_____
_____
_____
_____
_____
_____
_____
_____

I am thankful for

_____
_____
_____
_____
_____
_____
_____
_____
_____
_____
_____

Prayer requests

Date

Answered Prayers

Date

Things on my heart

_____
_____
_____
_____
_____
_____
_____

Highlights of this week

_____
_____
_____
_____
_____
_____
_____

> *Consider it pure joy, my brothers and sisters, whenever you face trials of many kinds, because you know that the testing of your faith produces perseverance. – James 1:2-3*

Teach me

_____
_____
_____
_____
_____
_____
_____
_____
_____
_____
_____

I am thankful for

_____
_____
_____
_____
_____
_____
_____
_____
_____
_____
_____

Prayer requests

Date

Answered Prayers

Date

Things on my heart

_____

_____

_____

_____

_____

_____

_____

Highlights of this week

_____

_____

_____

_____

_____

_____

_____

> But he said to me, "My grace is sufficient for you, for my power is made perfect in weakness." Therefore, I will boast all the more gladly about my weaknesses, so that Christ's power may rest on me. – 2 Corinthians 12:9

Teach me

I am thankful for

Prayer requests

Date

Answered Prayers

Date

Things on my heart

_____

_____

_____

_____

_____

_____

_____

Highlights of this week

_____

_____

_____

_____

_____

_____

_____

> I love you, LORD, my strength. The LORD is my rock, my fortress and my deliverer; my God is my rock, in whom I take refuge, my shield and the horn of my salvation, my stronghold.
>
> – Psalm 18:1-2

Teach me

I am thankful for

Prayer requests

Date

Answered Prayers

Date

Things on my heart

_____
_____
_____
_____
_____
_____
_____

Highlights of this week

_____
_____
_____
_____
_____
_____
_____

> The thief comes only to steal and kill and destroy; I have come that they may have life, and have it to the full.
>
> – John 10:10

Teach me

_____
_____
_____
_____
_____
_____
_____
_____
_____
_____
_____

I am thankful for

_____
_____
_____
_____
_____
_____
_____
_____
_____
_____

Prayer requests

Date

Answered Prayers

Date

Things on my heart

_____
_____
_____
_____
_____
_____
_____

Highlights of this week

_____
_____
_____
_____
_____
_____
_____

> You make known to me the path of life; you will fill me with joy in your presence, with eternal pleasures at your right hand.
> – Psalm 16:11

Teach me

_____
_____
_____
_____
_____
_____
_____
_____
_____
_____
_____

I am thankful for

_____
_____
_____
_____
_____
_____
_____
_____
_____
_____
_____

Prayer requests

Date

Answered Prayers

Date

Things on my heart   ## Highlights of this week

_____   _____

_____   _____

_____   _____

_____   _____

_____   _____

_____   _____

_____   _____

> *Even though I walk through the darkest valley, I will fear no evil, for you are with me; your rod and your staff, they comfort me. – Psalm 23:4*

Teach me

_____
_____
_____
_____
_____
_____
_____
_____
_____
_____
_____

I am thankful for

_____
_____
_____
_____
_____
_____
_____
_____
_____
_____
_____

Prayer requests

Date

Answered Prayers

Date

Things on my heart

Highlights of this week

_____
_____
_____
_____
_____
_____
_____

_____
_____
_____
_____
_____
_____
_____

> *I can do all this through him who gives me strength.*
> *– Philippians 4:13*

Teach me

_____
_____
_____
_____
_____
_____
_____
_____
_____

I am thankful for

_____
_____
_____
_____
_____
_____
_____
_____
_____

Prayer requests

Date

Answered Prayers

Date

Things on my heart

Highlights of this week

_____   _____

_____   _____

_____   _____

_____   _____

_____   _____

_____   _____

_____   _____

> For I am the LORD your God who takes hold of your right hand and says to you, Do not fear; I will help you.
>
> – Isaiah 41:13

Teach me

_____
_____
_____
_____
_____
_____
_____
_____
_____
_____

I am thankful for

_____
_____
_____
_____
_____
_____
_____
_____
_____
_____

Prayer requests

Date

Answered Prayers

Date

Things on my heart

Highlights of this week

_____

_____

_____

_____

_____

_____

_____

_____

_____

_____

_____

_____

_____

_____

> *And we know that in all things God works for the good of those who love him, who have been called according to his purpose.*
>
> – Romans 8:28

Teach me

I am thankful for

Prayer requests

Date

Answered Prayers

Date

Things on my heart

Highlights of this week

_____
_____
_____
_____
_____
_____
_____

_____
_____
_____
_____
_____
_____
_____

> *But as for me, I watch in hope for the LORD, I wait for God my Savior; my God will hear me. – Micah 7:7*

Teach me

I am thankful for

Prayer requests

Date

Answered Prayers

Date

Things on my heart

Highlights of this week

_____   _____

_____   _____

_____   _____

_____   _____

_____   _____

_____   _____

_____   _____

> I am the vine; you are the branches. If you remain in me and I in you, you will bear much fruit; apart from me you can do nothing. – John 15:5

Teach me

_____
_____
_____
_____
_____
_____
_____
_____
_____

I am thankful for

_____
_____
_____
_____
_____
_____
_____
_____

Prayer requests

Date

Answered Prayers

Date

Things on my heart

_____

_____

_____

_____

_____

_____

_____

Highlights of this week

_____

_____

_____

_____

_____

_____

_____

> *Show me your ways, LORD, teach me your paths. Guide me in your truth and teach me, for you are God my Savior, and my hope is in you all day long. – Psalm 25:4-5*

Teach me

_____
_____
_____
_____
_____
_____
_____
_____
_____
_____

I am thankful for

_____
_____
_____
_____
_____
_____
_____
_____
_____

Prayer requests

Date

Answered Prayers

Date

Things on my heart

Highlights of this week

_____

_____

_____

_____

_____

_____

_____

_____

_____

_____

_____

_____

_____

_____

> The LORD your God is with you, the Mighty Warrior who saves. He will take great delight in you; in his love he will no longer rebuke you, but will rejoice over you with singing.
> – Zephaniah 3:17

Teach me

I am thankful for

Prayer requests

Date

Answered Prayers

Date

Things on my heart

Highlights of this week

> So then, just as you received Christ Jesus as Lord, continue to live your lives in him, rooted and built up in him, strengthened in the faith as you were taught, and overflowing with thankfulness. – Colossians 2:6-7

Teach me

_____
_____
_____
_____
_____
_____
_____
_____
_____
_____
_____

I am thankful for

_____
_____
_____
_____
_____
_____
_____
_____
_____
_____
_____

Prayer requests

Date

Answered Prayers

Date

Things on my heart

Highlights of this week

_____

_____

_____

_____

_____

_____

_____

_____

Week of

> The LORD make his face shine on you and be gracious to you;
> the LORD turn his face toward you and give you peace.
>
> – Numbers 6:25-26

Teach me

I am thankful for

Prayer requests

Date

Answered Prayers

Date

Things on my heart

Highlights of this week

> Take delight in the LORD, and he will give you the desires of your heart. – Psalm 37:4

Teach me

_____
_____
_____
_____
_____
_____
_____
_____
_____
_____
_____

I am thankful for

_____
_____
_____
_____
_____
_____
_____
_____
_____

Prayer requests

Date

Answered Prayers

Date

Things on my heart

_____

_____

_____

_____

_____

_____

_____

Highlights of this week

_____

_____

_____

_____

_____

_____

_____

> But the fruit of the Spirit is love, joy, peace, forbearance, kindness, goodness, faithfulness, gentleness and self-control. Against such things there is no law. – Galatians 5:23-24

Teach me

_____
_____
_____
_____
_____
_____
_____
_____
_____

I am thankful for

_____
_____
_____
_____
_____
_____
_____
_____

Prayer requests

Date

Answered Prayers

Date

Things on my heart

Highlights of this week

_____

_____

_____

_____

_____

_____

_____

> *He has shown you, O man, what is good. And what does the LORD require of you? To act justly and to love mercy and to walk humbly with your God. – Micah 6:8*

Teach me

_____
_____
_____
_____
_____
_____
_____
_____
_____
_____

I am thankful for

_____
_____
_____
_____
_____
_____
_____
_____
_____

Prayer requests

Date

Answered Prayers

Date

Things on my heart

Highlights of this week

_____

_____

_____

_____

_____

_____

_____

> *A cheerful heart is good medicine, but a crushed spirit dries up the bones. – Proverbs 17:22*

Teach me

_____
_____
_____
_____
_____
_____
_____
_____
_____
_____

I am thankful for

_____
_____
_____
_____
_____
_____
_____
_____
_____
_____

Prayer requests

Date

Answered Prayers

Date

Things on my heart

Highlights of this week

_____ _____

_____ _____

_____ _____

_____ _____

_____ _____

_____ _____

_____ _____

_____ _____

Now to him who is able to do immeasurably more than all we ask or imagine, according to his power that is at work within us, to him be glory in the church and in Christ Jesus throughout all generations, for ever and ever! Amen. – Ephesians 3:20-21

Teach me

_____
_____
_____
_____
_____
_____
_____
_____
_____
_____

I am thankful for

_____
_____
_____
_____
_____
_____
_____
_____
_____
_____

Prayer requests

Date

Answered Prayers

Date

Things on my heart

Highlights of this week

> However, as it is written: "What no eye has seen, what no ear has heard, and what no human mind has conceived" -- the things God has prepared for those who love him.
>
> – 1 Corinthians 2:9

Teach me

_____
_____
_____
_____
_____
_____
_____
_____

I am thankful for

_____
_____
_____
_____
_____
_____
_____

Prayer requests

Date

Answered Prayers

Date

Things on my heart

_____
_____
_____
_____
_____
_____
_____
_____

Highlights of this week

_____
_____
_____
_____
_____
_____
_____
_____

> *You will seek me and find me when you seek me with all your heart. – Jeremiah 29:13*

Teach me

_____
_____
_____
_____
_____
_____
_____
_____
_____
_____

I am thankful for

_____
_____
_____
_____
_____
_____
_____
_____

Prayer requests

Date

Answered Prayers

Date

Things on my heart

_____

_____

_____

_____

_____

_____

_____

Highlights of this week

_____

_____

_____

_____

_____

_____

_____

> *He saved us, not because of righteous things we had done, but because of his mercy. He saved us through the washing of rebirth and renewal by the Holy Spirit. – Titus 3:5*

Teach me

_____
_____
_____
_____
_____
_____
_____
_____
_____
_____
_____

I am thankful for

_____
_____
_____
_____
_____
_____
_____
_____
_____
_____

Prayer requests

Date

Answered Prayers

Date

Things on my heart

_____
_____
_____
_____
_____
_____
_____

Highlights of this week

_____
_____
_____
_____
_____
_____
_____

> Therefore, there is now no condemnation for those who are in Christ Jesus., because through Christ Jesus the law of the Spirit who gives life has set you free from the law of sin and death.
>
> – Romans 8:1-2

Teach me

_____
_____
_____
_____
_____
_____
_____
_____
_____
_____
_____

I am thankful for

_____
_____
_____
_____
_____
_____
_____
_____
_____
_____

Prayer requests

Date

Answered Prayers

Date

Things on my heart

Highlights of this week

> Some trust in chariots and some in horses, but we trust in the name of the LORD our God. They are brought to their knees and fall, but we rise up and stand firm. – Psalm 20:7-8

Teach me

_____
_____
_____
_____
_____
_____
_____
_____
_____
_____

I am thankful for

_____
_____
_____
_____
_____
_____
_____
_____
_____
_____

Prayer requests

Date

Answered Prayers

Date

Things on my heart

Highlights of this week

_____   _____

_____   _____

_____   _____

_____   _____

_____   _____

_____   _____

_____   _____

_____   _____

> *Do not conform to the pattern of this world, but be transformed by the renewing of your mind. Then you will be able to test and approve what God's will is--his good, pleasing and perfect will. – Romans 12:2*

Teach me

_____
_____
_____
_____
_____
_____
_____
_____
_____
_____
_____

I am thankful for

_____
_____
_____
_____
_____
_____
_____
_____
_____
_____

Prayer requests

Date

Answered Prayers

Date

Things on my heart

Highlights of this week

_____
_____
_____
_____
_____
_____
_____

_____
_____
_____
_____
_____
_____
_____

Until now you have not asked for anything in my name.
Ask and you will receive, and your joy will be complete.

– John 16:24

Teach me

I am thankful for

Prayer requests

Date

Answered Prayers

Date

Things on my heart

_____
_____
_____
_____
_____
_____
_____

Highlights of this week

_____
_____
_____
_____
_____
_____
_____

Week of

> *But seek first his kingdom and his righteousness, and all these things will be given to you as well. – Matthew 6:33*

Teach me

I am thankful for

Prayer requests

Date

Answered Prayers

Date

Things on my heart

_____

_____

_____

_____

_____

_____

_____

Highlights of this week

_____

_____

_____

_____

_____

_____

_____

> Therefore, do not worry about tomorrow, for tomorrow will worry about itself. Each day has enough trouble of its own.
> – Matthew 6:34

Teach me

_____
_____
_____
_____
_____
_____
_____
_____
_____
_____

I am thankful for

_____
_____
_____
_____
_____
_____
_____
_____
_____
_____
_____

Prayer requests

Date

Answered Prayers

Date

Things on my heart

Highlights of this week

_____

_____

_____

_____

_____

_____

_____

> Surely God is my salvation; I will trust and not be afraid. The LORD, the LORD himself, is my strength and my defense; he has become my salvation. – Isaiah 12:2

Teach me

I am thankful for

Prayer requests

Date

Answered Prayers

Date

Things on my heart

Highlights of this week

_____
_____
_____
_____
_____
_____
_____

_____
_____
_____
_____
_____
_____
_____

Week of ⟩

> *Give thanks in all circumstances; for this is God's will for you in Christ Jesus. – 1 Thessalonians 5:18*

Teach me

_____
_____
_____
_____
_____
_____
_____
_____
_____
_____

I am thankful for

_____
_____
_____
_____
_____
_____
_____
_____
_____

Prayer requests

Date

Answered Prayers

Date

Things on my heart

Highlights of this week

_____

_____

_____

_____

_____

_____

_____

Made in the USA
Columbia, SC
09 December 2022

73098618R00061